DEVELOPING LITERACY

**Photocopiable
teaching resources
for literacy**

G000299028

SENTENCE STRUCTURE AND PUNCTUATION

Ages 7–8

Christine Moorcroft

A & C Black • London

Contents

Punctuation

Instruction and information sentences

Poetic sentences

Reprinted 2011
Published 2008 by A & C Black Publishers Limited
36 Soho Square, London W1D 3QY
www.acblack.com

ISBN 978-0-7136-8456-8

Copyright text © Christine Moorcroft 2008
Copyright illustrations © Andy Keylock 2008
Copyright cover illustration © Jan McCafferty 2008
Editor: Dodi Beardshaw
Design: HL Studios, Oxford and Susan McIntyre

The author and publishers would like to thank Ray Barker and Fleur Lawrence for their advice in producing this series of books.

A CIP catalogue record for this book is available from the British Library.

Printed and bound in Great Britain by Martins the Printers, Berwick-on-Tweed.

A & C Black uses paper produced with elemental chlorine-free pulp, harvested from managed sustainable forests.

Introduction

100% New Developing Literacy Sentence Structure and Punctuation is a series of seven photocopiable activity books for developing children's understanding of sentences and their ability to form sentences.

The books provide learning activities to support strand 11 (Sentence structure and punctuation) of the literacy objectives of the Primary Framework for Literacy and Mathematics.

The structure of **100% New Developing Literacy Sentence Structure and Punctuation Ages 7–8** is designed to complement the structure of the Primary Framework for Ages 7–8, which focuses on the following types of text:

- narrative (stories with familiar settings, myths and legends, adventure and mystery, authors and letters, dialogue and plays)
- non-fiction (reports, instructions, information texts)
- poetry (poems to perform, shape poetry and calligrams, language play).

100% New Developing Literacy Sentence Structure and Punctuation Ages 7–8 addresses the following objectives from the Primary Framework:

- show relationships of time, reason and cause through subordination and connectives;
- compose sentences using adjectives, verbs and nouns for precision, clarity and impact;
- clarify meaning through the use of exclamation marks and speech marks.

The sentence-level activities provided in this book support the children's reading and writing across different text-types, with a specific emphasis on those listed above: for example, the first section, **Narrative sentences** (pages 12–21), focuses mainly on sentences in the past tense (used in narrative writing), what characters did, where, when and why. The second section, **Sentence sense** (pages 22–26), supports this by helping the children to understand how sentences are structured and how they work: it also provides a sound foundation for non-fiction writing. **All kinds of words** (pages 27–41) and **Punctuation** (pages 42–52) support both narrative and non-fiction writing. **Instruction and information sentences** (pages 53–60) supports non-fiction writing (instructions, explanations, information texts and non-chronological reports). It develops the children's understanding of the different types of sentences used in different types of writing, including the use of the first and third person and the narrative and command forms of verbs. The final section, **Poetic sentences** (pages 61–64), is linked to the language of poetry, how sentences can be used in poetry, the effect of writing without sentences and the layout of poetic sentences.

Through the activities the children learn:

- the essentials of a sentence;
- how to make a group of words into a sentence;
- how to demarcate sentences with capital letters and full stops, question marks or exclamation marks;
- how to use speech marks in dialogue;
- how to set out dialogue for a play script;
- about using commas in lists and to separate parts of a sentence;
- about the present and past tenses and how to use them consistently;
- about different types of word (for example, proper nouns, verbs, adjectives, personal and possessive pronouns and words for joining sentences and for saying how, when, where and why);
- about the first, second and third person;
- about choosing the most effective verbs and adjectives;

Some of activities can be carried out with the whole class, some are more suitable for small groups and others are for individual work. Most of the activities require a written response but some are presented in the form of games. They can be used for different purposes: to introduce skills need for a particular type of writing, to support writing or to help with the assessment of children's progress.

Reading

Most children will be able to carry out the activities independently. It is expected that some children might need help in reading some of the instructions on the sheets and that someone will read them to, or with, them.

Organisation

The activities require very few resources besides pencils, crayons, scissors, glue and word-banks. Other materials are specified in the Teachers' Notes at the bottom of each page: for example, information books and dictionaries.

Extension activities

Most of the activity sheets end with a challenge ('Now try this!') which reinforces and extends the children's learning and provides the teacher with an opportunity for assessment. These more challenging activities might be appropriate for only a few children; it is not expected that the whole class should complete them. On some pages there is space for the children to complete the extension activities, but others will require a notebook or a separate sheet of paper.

Accompanying CD

The enclosed CD-ROM contains electronic versions of all the activity sheets in the book for printing, editing, saving or display on an interactive whiteboard. Our unique browser-based interface makes it easy to select pages and to modify them to suit individual pupils' needs. See page 11 for further details.

Notes on the activities

These notes for the teacher expand upon those which are provided at the bottom of the activity pages. They give ideas and suggestions for making the most of the activity sheet, including suggestions for the whole-class introduction, the plenary session and for follow-up work using an adapted version of the activity sheet. To help teachers to select appropriate learning experiences for their pupils, the activities are grouped into sections within each book but the pages need not be presented in the order in which they appear, unless otherwise stated.

Narrative sentences

The activities in this section mainly feature sentences in the past tense. They support text-level work on narrative and provide opportunities for the children to identify, demarcate or complete sentences, check sentences for sense and use sentences as models for writing their own. The present and past tenses are included and the children practise forming these and develop their understanding of the need to use them consistently. They learn about different forms and uses of the past and present tenses, choosing the most effective verbs and using connectives to indicate sequence, place, reason and purpose.

On your screen (page 12) reinforces the children's understanding of a sentence. They are required to identify the ends of sentences and the beginnings of new ones and to demarcate them using capital letters and full stops. It is useful to point out that punctuation is a useful tool which helps children to write what they mean and for others to understand what they mean. In addition to using the page as directed, on another copy you could also insert full stops, commas and capital letters in the wrong places and ask the children to read the passage, for example:

> The wind became. Stronger it was, blowing. Me, back, but I had to reach. The other side of the beach sprays. Of sand dashed onto my. Face, I kept my mouth, tightly. Closed, my eyes hurt. There was sand in my mouth, then my foot. Struck something. Hard, it felt. Like metal.

Discuss the changes in meaning.

This and other passages from stories could be scanned and displayed on an interactive whiteboard. Using a split screen, you could display the unaltered and the corrected versions simultaneously for comparison.

Past and present: 1 and 2 (pages 13–14) reinforce the children's understanding of the past and present tenses. It can be linked with word-level work on adding suffixes to form the past tense and on irregular verbs in which a different word is used for the past tense or when the spelling remains the same but the pronunciation changes (for example, *read*).
Past and present: 1 is concerned with the simple present and past tenses: *walk/walked, say/said, do/did, run/ran* and so on.
Past and present: 2 focuses on the present and past tense

formed with auxiliary verbs: *am/are/is/was/were walking, saying, doing, running* and so on. Link this with work on spelling – adding the suffixes *-ed* and *-ing* and changing the ending of the root word where necessary (doubling the final consonant, dropping the final *e*).

Into the past (page 15) helps the children to understand the purpose and use of the past and present tenses in writing. It introduces the consistent use of a tense in narrative. During the plenary session you could ask volunteers to read the passage in the present and then the past tense for comparison.

Time travel (page 16) develops skills in using tenses consistently. You could also provide speech bubble-shaped cards on which the children can write other words for the robots (choosing either the present or past tense) and then pass to a friend to check that the tense is the same throughout. These could then be mixed up and sorted into two sets: past and present.

Action sentences (page 17) is about choosing expressive verbs for movement in order to create an impression of subjects. It provides lists of verbs and settings from which the children can choose the most appropriate. They could begin by matching the subjects to the settings and then selecting the best verb. During the plenary session discuss why they chose these verbs and the impression they create. The children could key in sentences containing verbs such as *go*, *say* or *had* from stories they have written. Display them, one at a time, on an interactive whiteboard and invite suggestions for different verbs. Discuss the effects of these verbs and choose the most expressive for the context.

Setting sentences (page 18) is about choosing expressive verbs to use instead of *was*. It provides sections of sentences to describe places using expressive verbs. The children are asked to match up a building, a word for *was* and a place: for example, *Valley farm nestled in a hollow by a stream, High House perched on a hilltop overlooking the village, Elm Street School squatted among gas works and old warehouses, Station Cottages stretched along the old railway, Priory Mews clung to the wall of the church, Rook Castle guarded the town.* The children could also try swapping the verbs, or trying new ones, to compare the effects. The children could begin a section for a class thesaurus listing verbs to replace is/was in sentences saying where something is/was situated. Help them to find examples in a range of texts, including fiction, advertisements (printed or audio), leaflets, documentary film voice-overs, information books, poems and Internet sources.

Time sentences (page 19) focuses on the use of adverbial phrases of time, although this term is not yet introduced. It develops the children's understanding of the purposes of words and groups of words in sentences. The children could begin by reading each example and saying whether or not it is a sentence. Draw out that they are all sentences and that the children are going to add extra information about when the action took place.

Place to place (page 20) focuses on the use of adverbial phrases of place, although this term is not yet introduced. It develops the children's understanding of the purposes of words and groups of words in sentences. The children could begin by reading each example and saying whether or not it is a sentence. Draw out that they are all sentences and that the children are going to add extra information – about where the action took place.

One thing after another (page 21) develops the children's understanding about how words are used in recounts to show the order in which events happen. They could also create a personal word-bank of useful words to use in stories for showing when things happen. As a further extension activity, you could  ask the children to add information to simple sentences such as *Rani bought an ice cream*. Type up the sentences, display them on an interactive whiteboard and make copies for the children to alter in different ways. Ask them to add words that say when, how *and* where (and even why).

Sentence sense

The activities in this section reinforce the children's previous learning about recognising a sentence. They have opportunities to construct compound sentences using subordination (and the use of connectives) involving place, time and reason and to find out about the essential words in sentences.

Shrink it (page 22) reinforces the children's understanding of sentences. They are required to delete different words from a sentence and to check if it is still a sentence. During the plenary session, ask the children what kinds of words cannot be deleted from a sentence. Draw out that adjectives and words for time and place can be omitted but that verbs and, in most sentences, some nouns and pronouns cannot.

Shrinking sentences (page 23) helps the children to recognise the essential words in sentences. They are asked to delete all the non-essential words in a sentence. During the plenary session, when the children could read out their shortened sentences, challenge the others to shorten them even more, if this is feasible. Ask them which type of word can never be taken out of a sentence. Draw out that the verb is essential and that another word which is usually necessary is the noun or pronoun for the person or object doing the action, or having the action done to him/her, it/them; adjectives and words for time and place can be omitted. You could also display a long sentence each day and challenge the children to shrink it to the shortest possible sentence.

Growing sentences (page 24) develops the children's understanding of how sentences work and how to construct compound sentences. This is the opposite process to the one which the children practised on pages 22–23. Use the completed example to model the way in which a sentence can be extended, and discuss the effect of this. Draw out that by adding to a sentence the writer can create an impression or give information. You could set a challenge for the children – to create the longest possible sentence. Draw out, however, that it is not always a good thing to write very long sentences. Sometimes short ones are more effective.

A simple sentence contains one clause. A compound sentence contains more than one clause of equal value (ie, there are no subordinate clauses): for example, *The adults were chatting and the children were playing*. A complex sentence (also called a multiple sentence) contains at least one main clause and at least one subordinate clause: for example, *The girl ate the sandwiches which her father had prepared for her*. The subordinate clause (italicised) does not make sense as a sentence. A main clause makes sense on its own as a sentence but a subordinate clause depends on the main clause for its meaning.

Because (page 25) develops the children's understanding of the purposes of connectives. Ask them about words they have used for joining sentences. Introduce the term *connective* and point out that connectives can show *when*, *where*, *how* or *why* something happened. Can the children spell *because*? Ask them for examples of sentences using *because* and challenge them to take out the word *because* and split the sentences into two shorter ones. This could be linked with the writing of instructions – adding an explanation: for example, *Do not bake for too long as this can lead to a bitter taste.*

That's why (page 26) develops the children's understanding of the purposes of connectives. Remind them of the connectives they have used for joining sentences, including *because*. Tell them that they are going to use some other connectives which show purposes – what someone does something for. Ask them to read the words on the word-bank and to notice that one of the connectives is made up of three words (*in order to*). Ask them to choose the best connective to help them to add a purpose to each sentence.

All kinds of words

This section is about the different types of word in a sentence. It focuses on similarities between different types of words and introduces their names: *noun, pronoun, verb, connective*. The children develop their understanding of the purposes of different words in a sentence.

The noun test (page 27) reinforces the children's previous learning about nouns and introduces a test they can use to check if a word is a noun. You could also discuss why *a* is used with some nouns and *an* with others: note the difficulty in enunciating a noun beginning with a vowel after *a* (for example, *a orange, a apple, a egg, a elephant, a icicle, a oblong, a oval, a umbrella*).

The right noun (page 28) focuses on nouns with similar meanings. The children could also add *a* or *an* before each noun and apply the 'noun test'.

Proper noun challenge (page 29) reinforces the children's previous learning about proper nouns. It is useful to remind them that proper nouns are names, which begin with a capital letter. The children could also play this game using a blank grid and selecting letters by opening a book at a random page and using the first letter on the page. The headings on the chart could be changed: for example, *Country, River, Television programme, Song, Singer, Football team, Footballer*.

Wobbling words (page 30) focuses on the personal pronouns *he, him, she, her, it, they* and *them*. You could reinforce the children's learning during the plenary session by saying the names of things or people and asking them for a word to use instead. Ask them how they know when to use *he, him, she, her, it, they* and *them*.

Pronouns (page 31) extends the children's understanding of personal pronouns: *I, me, us, we, he, him, she, her, it, they* and *them*. The children select the appropriate personal pronoun to replace each noun. It is useful to discuss the altered sentences and ask whether replacing the nouns

with pronouns improved them. Did it make them easier to read or to understand? Did it make them sound better? Draw out that if no nouns are used we cannot tell what is meant by some of the pronouns.

Instead of nouns (page 32) uses a Greek myth to provide practice in replacing nouns with pronouns. After the children have completed the passage, ask them to take turns to read parts of it to the class. It is useful to point out that some nouns have not been replaced with pronouns and to discuss why not. Draw out that some nouns are necessary so that the reader knows whom the story is about and who does the action in each sentence. You could display this or another passage on the interactive whiteboard and ask the children to replace all the nouns with pronouns then re-read the passage. Ask them if this is an improvement, and why not. Save this version and make a copy on which they can then replace all the pronouns with nouns. Discuss whether this is better. Display the original alongside the two altered versions and discuss where it is appropriate to use pronouns, and why.

Belonging (page 33) is about possessive pronouns. It develops the children's awareness of words to denote belonging. You could introduce the activity by saying the names of things or people and asking them for a word to use for something belonging to them: for example, *Jason's coat, Leah's pencil, Sally and Mike's table, the footballer's head, the car's roof*. Ask them how they know when to use *his, her, its* or *their*. You could also ask what some of these owners themselves would say about their belongings and about those of someone they are talking to (*my coat, my pencil, our table, your head, your hat*).

Words for describing (page 34) reinforces the children's learning about adjectives by focusing on the nouns they describe. It develops the children's understanding that there are different types of words and that they are used for different purposes in sentences. This page could be linked with the discussion of characters and settings of stories.

Describe and draw (page 35) reinforces the children's learning about adjectives by asking them to choose adjectives to describe nouns in captions. They could also be given a treasure hunt in which they have to find objects to match descriptions, such as long and green, brown and crisp, soft and black, warm and golden.

All change (page 36) reinforces the children's learning about adjectives by asking them to change the adjectives in captions in order to describe the objects in the pictures. It could be linked with work on persuasive texts in which the children could change unpleasant descriptive words to make something sound pleasant.

Verb detective (page 37) reinforces the children's learning about verbs by asking them to identify the verbs in a text. It is useful to point out that some verbs denote *being* rather than any movement or obvious action: for example, *to be, to live, to exist*. This page could be linked with text-level work on myths and legends.

Verb sort (page 38) reinforces the children's learning about verbs and nouns by asking them to sort a set of cards according to whether they are nouns or verbs and then to use them to complete a sentence. During the plenary session, invite volunteers to give sentences they can remember from the game. Draw out that sentences can say silly things but still make sense as sentences.

Smart verbs (page 39) develops the children's learning about verbs by asking them to choose appropriate verbs to fill gaps in sentences. It focuses on verbs with similar meanings but which can create different effects. Ask the children if the completed captions are sentences, and how they can tell. Draw out that they make sense and tell the reader something.

Vivid verbs (page 40) develops the children's learning about verbs by asking them to groups verbs according to meaning. This can be linked with work in fiction or poetry writing on choosing words for their effect. You could create an interactive classroom display on to which the children could fix verbs written in bright colours under headings such as *Talk, Fall, Write, Look*. Challenge them to find new verbs which match each heading.

Join-up jigsaw (page 41) is about connectives, although this term is not yet introduced to the children. These words help the children to compose compound and complex sentences, some of which include subordination involving time and reason. Ask them to read the two sections of each sentence and ask if they could be sentences in their own right, and how we can tell. Scan pictures of objects and scenes and display them on an interactive whiteboard, with text boxes in which the children can write adjectives. Ask them to write two adjectives to describe each item or scene. Save all their pairs of adjectives for comparison during the plenary session.

Punctuation

These activities consolidate the children's understanding of the use of a capital letter and a full stop to demarcate the beginning and end of a sentence, an exclamation mark to mark the end of an exclamation and a question mark to end a question, as well as the use of commas to separate items in a list and to separate or enclose parts of a sentence. Speech marks, introduced in the dialogue activities (pages 46–51) are revisited and the children learn about punctuation before and after speech marks.

Exclamation words (page 42) shows the children how to form an exclamation mark. You could point out that part of an exclamation mark is the same as a full stop because it is usually used at the end of a sentence. The part above the full stop shows that the sentence is an exclamation. Explain what this means using examples such as *Help! Come here! Go away! Stop!* As a homework activity the children could collect examples of exclamations from comic books and newspaper cartoons. This can be linked with text-level work on jokes and humour.

Ha, ha! (page 43) helps the children to distinguish between sentences which are questions and others which are exclamations. This can be linked with text-level work on jokes and humour. The children could begin a class joke collection, either as a display or on a computer. Encourage them to check that the questions have question marks and the funny answers have exclamation marks.

End points (page 44) consolidates the children's understanding of punctuation at the ends of sentences: when to use a full stop, an exclamation mark or a question mark. You could point out that part of a question mark is the same as a full stop because it belongs at the end of a sentence. The part above the full stop shows that the sentence is a question. Also point out that part of an exclamation mark is the same as a full stop because it belongs at the end of a sentence. The part above the full stop shows that the sentence is an exclamation.

Knock, knock (page 45) provides practice in writing dialogue using speech bubbles. It reinforces the children's learning that the spoken words are enclosed in a speech bubble, preparing them for using speech marks for the same purpose in text. The children could also make a class collection of 'knock, knock' jokes, written using speech bubbles and/or speech marks.

Story talk (page 46) introduces speech marks for enclosing spoken words in text. The children are asked to identify the spoken words in a passage. Note that this story is printed with only single quotation marks, not double as used elsewhere.

They could first practise writing speech marks. You could present the marks as *66* and *99* because the first resembles the number 66 in orientation and the second resembles the number 99. Encourage them to write the speech marks in line with the tops of the tallest letters.

If animals could talk (page 47) is about the use of speech marks to replace speech bubbles. The children should write only the spoken words between the speech marks. You could draw attention to the other punctuation: the use of a comma at the end of spoken words followed by *said* or any other verb for *said*.

Television talk (page 48) focuses on dialogue represented in the form of a script. The children convert the script into dialogue using speech marks. It is useful to point out how the spoken words are represented on paper to show who is speaking and what they say. A useful follow-up activity would be to listen to a short television or radio interview and write what the people said. Working in pairs, the children could record the interview and then replay it, stopping to transcribe it.

Scriptwriter (page 49) is about changing dialogue with speech marks into a play script. The children are required to identify the spoken words in the story and write them in play script form. As this traditional story continues, the man pulls his coat tightly around himself to keep warm in the strong wind. The sun shines so brightly that the weather becomes extremely hot and the man has to take off his coat – so the sun won the argument. They could repeat this process with other fables, since fables are usually very short. See http://www.aesopfables.com/ or http://www.purr-n-fur.org.uk/fabled/fontaine/fontaine.html. You might find it useful to copy and alter these to simplify the language. To help the children to set out playscripts, create a table in Word, with a narrow column for the names of the characters speaking and a wider column for the spoken words.

Speech marks (page 50) and **Speech on the page** (page 51) reinforce the children's learning about dialogue and focuses on the positioning of speech marks with relation to the spoken words and the surrounding text. Point out that when the spoken words are followed by *said* or a similar word the full stop at the end of the spoken words is changed to a comma (but note that question marks and exclamation marks are retained).

The comma store (page 52) reinforces the children's learning about how commas help the reader to make sense of a sentence containing a list. You could demonstrate how it is used by

reading the first example as it is written, pausing where the comma should be. Ask them if this sounds right, then invite a volunteer to read it correctly. Ask the others what was the difference and draw out that when it was read correctly there was a pause after *oranges*. Point out that the sentence contains a list and remind the children that there should be a comma after each item in a list, except for the last one, where *and* is used.

Instruction and information sentences

This section is about sentences in the imperative (command) form and sentences which give information. Also included are writing notes (including abbreviations) and the use of the first, second and third person. The activities support the writing of non-fiction.

The first person (page 53) reinforces the children's learning about the use of capital *I* to represent their name and about the pronouns *I*, *me*, *we* and *us*. It introduces the term *the first person*. This activity could be linked with work on letters and diaries and discussing why they are written in the first person.

The second person (page 54) reinforces the children's learning about the pronoun *you*. It introduces the term *the second person*. This activity could be linked with work on instructions and discussing why they can be written in the second person.

The third person (page 55) reinforces the children's learning about the pronouns *he*, *him*, *she*, *her*, *it*, *they* and *them*. It introduces the term *the third person*. This activity could be linked with work on non-chronological report and information texts and discussing why they are written in the third person.

Reporting sentences (page 56) helps the children to recognise the style of a non-chronological report. Draw out how these sentences are different from the sentences used in instructions or recounts by focusing on the person and on the form and tense of the verb.

Do this and **Command verbs** (pages 57–58) focus on the verbs used in instructions. They develop the children's awareness of the style of sentence used in instructions. The children could discuss the sentences with a partner and then collaborate on the answers they write. During the plenary session it is useful to focus on the verbs used. Draw out that they are in the command form – they tell the reader what to do. These activities can be linked with text-level work on writing instructions.

That's the way (page 59) reinforces the children's learning about the verbs used in instructions and develops their understanding of how to write instruction sentences. This activity can support work in geography on following maps to find the way to places and using a map to help in giving directions. It can also be linked with work in design and technology in which they write a report about what they have made and then convert it into instructions or a recipe which someone else could follow. The children could type up their recount of a process. Select recounts to display on an interactive whiteboard and invite volunteers to take turns to change sentences into instruction (command) form. Similarly, they could convert recipes into recounts.

Go with the flow (page 60) reinforces the children's learning about connective words in compound sentences involving time. It is useful to draw out that these words help to communicate information about the order in which events happen, especially in a fiction or non-fiction recount.

Poetic sentences

These activities focus on the use of sentences in poems and the types of sentences found in poems. The children explore the use of language for creating effects and consolidate their understanding of sentences.

Sentences in poems (page 61) develops the children's appreciation that poems can be written in sentences but that some are not. They identify the lines of poetry which make up a sentence and those which do not. During the plenary session, ask them why the parts which are not sentences are included in poems. Draw out that poets use words to create effects as well as to tell the reader something and that these effects help to communicate feelings and to create an atmosphere and mood (humour, excitement, sadness and so on). Also note that sentences in poems do not always end with a full stop and that sometimes they can extend over several lines – even over an entire verse.

Non-sentences and **Poem without a sentence** (pages 62–63) are about how poets choose the most important words to use and omit others from sentences in order to create an affect. These activities can help the children to understand the difference between prose and poetry. They also remind them of the difference between a line of text and a sentence and can be used to support text-level work on reading poetry, in which they learn to appreciate the effects created by poems and identify the ways in which poets create these effects.

A sentence in any shape (page 64) helps the children to identify sentences in poems, whatever the layout. It can be linked with text-level work on writing calligrams and shape poems, which may or may not contain sentences. You could model how to write interesting sentences using the interactive whiteboard. Begin with *A snake went across the grass* and ask the children to think of a better verb than *went* to say how a snake might move: for example, *slithered, wriggled, slid*. Discuss a more interesting way to say *across the garden*. You could add adjectives and other words to give the reader an impression of the garden and a picture of the snake slithering: *between the tall blades of grass*. The final sentence might be *The snake slithered between the tall blades of grass*. Ask the children which sentence gives them a clearer picture of the scene, and how.

Using the CD-ROM

The PC CD-ROM included with this book contains an easy-to-use software program that allows you to print out pages from the book, to view them (e.g. on an interactive whiteboard) or to customise the activities to suit the needs of your pupils.

Getting started

It's easy to run the software. Simply insert the CD-ROM into your CD drive and the disk should autorun and launch the interface in your web browser.

If the disk does not autorun, open 'My Computer' and select the CD drive, then open the file 'start.html'.

Please note: this CD-ROM is designed for use on a PC. It will also run on most Apple Macintosh computers in Safari however, due to the differences between Mac and PC fonts, you may experience some unavoidable variations in the typography and page layouts of the activity sheets.

The Menu screen

Four options are available to you from the main menu screen.

The first option takes you to the Activity Sheets screen, where you can choose an activity sheet to edit or print out using Microsoft Word.

(If you do not have the Microsoft Office suite, you might like to consider using OpenOffice instead. This is a multi-platform and multi-lingual office suite, and an 'open-source' project. It is compatible with all other major office suites, and the product is free to download, use and distribute. The homepage for OpenOffice on the Internet is: www.openoffice.org.)

The second option on the main menu screen opens a PDF file of the entire book using Adobe Reader (see below). This format is ideal for printing out copies of the activity sheets or for displaying them, for example on an interactive whiteboard.

The third option allows you to choose a page to edit from a text-only list of the activity sheets, as an alternative to the graphical interface on the Activity Sheets screen.

Adobe Reader is free to download and to use. If it is not already installed on your computer, the fourth link takes you to the download page on the Adobe website.

You can also navigate directly to any of the three screens at any time by using the tabs at the top.

The Activity Sheets screen

This screen shows thumbnails of all the activity sheets in the book. Rolling the mouse over a thumbnail highlights the page number and also brings up a preview image of the page.

Click on the thumbnail to open a version of the page in Microsoft Word (or an equivalent software program, see above.) The full range of editing tools are available to you here to customise the page to suit the needs of your particular pupils. You can print out copies of the page or save a copy of your edited version onto your computer.

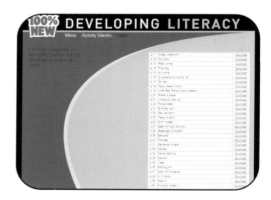

The Index screen

This is a text-only version of the Activity Sheets screen described above. Choose an activity sheet and click on the 'download' link to open a version of the page in Microsoft Word to edit or print out.

Technical support

If you have any questions regarding the *100% New Developing Literacy* or *Developing Mathematics* software, please email us at the address below. We will get back to you as quickly as possible.

educationalsales@acblack.com

On your screen

- **Read the words on the screen.**
- **Write the sentences.**

Don't forget the full stops and capital letters.

the wind became stronger it was blowing me back but I had to reach the other side of the beach sprays of sand dashed on to my face I kept my mouth tightly closed my eyes hurt there was sand in my mouth then my foot struck something hard it felt like metal

NOW TRY THIS!

- **What might happen next?**
- **Write a sentence.**

Teachers' note Give the children a copy of this page and ask them to follow the passage as you read it. Read it without pausing at the ends of sentences. Read the final sentence as if there is something to follow. Ask the children if they think it sounded right. What was wrong with it? Why do you read it like that and how does punctuation help? Model this with the first sentence.

100% New Developing Literacy
Sentence Structure and
Punctuation: Ages 7–8
© A & C BLACK

Past and present: 1

The ⬚past⬚ has happened.

The ⬚present⬚ is happening now.

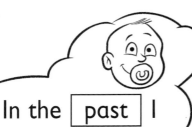

In the ⬚past⬚ I ⬚was⬚ a baby.

At ⬚present⬚ I ⬚am⬚ eight years old.

• **Fill in the gaps.**

Past	Present
I lived in Wales.	I _____ in England.
I _____ to nursery.	I go to school.
I liked my teddy.	I _____ my computer.
I _____ a tricycle.	I ride a bike.
I slept in a cot.	I _____ in a bed.
I _____ from a bottle.	I drink from a cup.
I _____ with rattles.	I play with toy cars.
I ate baby food.	I _____ all kinds of food.
I had no teeth.	I _____ a lot of teeth.
I _____ a baby gro.	I wear jeans.

NOW TRY THIS!

• **Write three sentences about these:**

schools in the past

schools in the present

Teachers' note Remind the children that we change the words for what we do depending on whether we are doing it now or have already done it. If appropriate, introduce the term *verb* for these words. You could link this with word-level work on adding the suffix -ed and on how words change according to meaning.

100% New Developing Literacy
Sentence Structure and
Punctuation: Ages 7–8
© A & C BLACK

The | past | was happening.

The | present | is happening now.

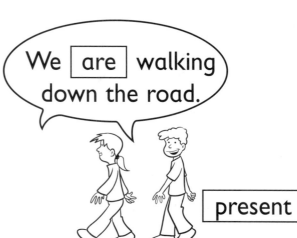

We | are | walking down the road.

present

We | were | walking down the road.

past

- **Write these sentences in the present tense.**
- **Circle the words you changed.**

1 I was eating my breakfast.

_____

2 We were going to town.

_____

3 He was looking for his coat.

_____

4 They were sitting at the table.

_____

5 You were riding Henry's bike.

_____

6 Dad was reading a story.

_____

NOW TRY THIS!

- **Write two sentences about what you are doing now.**
- **Write them in the past tense.**

Teachers' note Remind the children of their previous learning about the past tenses of verbs and introduce the use of auxiliary verbs like *am, is, are, was* and *were* for forming the present and past tenses: *I am talking, You were singing* and so on. You could link this with word-level work on adding the suffix *-ing*.

100% New Developing Literacy
Sentence Structure and
Punctuation: Ages 7–8
© A & C BLACK

Into the past

The Ancient Greek myths are from the past.

The passage is written in the present.

Change it to the past.

- **Circle the words you will change.**

Rewrite the passage.

In the land of Colchis there is a fleece from a golden ram. A dragon that never sleeps guards it.

Jason says he will go and get the golden fleece. He has an enormous ship built, and names it *Argo*.

Finally the ship is ready and Jason sets off with his crew, the Argonauts. As soon as they land in Colchis, Jason sends a message to the King. He says that he has come for the golden fleece. The King says he can take it if he can complete two tasks: yoke two fire-breathing bulls to a plough and kill a dragon, then plant its teeth in the ground.

NOW TRY THIS!

- **What do you think happened next?**
- **Write three sentences in the past tense.**

Teachers' note Discuss stories that children know, then ask them if these are written in the present or the past tense and how they can tell. Invite volunteers to give example verbs. Read the passage with them. How can we tell that it is in the present tense? How could it be changed to the past tense? What is the first word you need to change and what would you change it to?

100% New Developing Literacy Sentence Structure and Punctuation: Ages 7–8 © A & C BLACK

Time travel

The robots can only speak in the ⟨past⟩ tense.

- Change their words to the ⟨present⟩.
- Underline the words to change.
- Write what the robots should say.

> The sun was shining all day. The heat was melting my feet.

_____
_____
_____
_____

> I was dancing. I liked doing the foxtrot but foxes didn't trot.

_____
_____
_____
_____

> I was writing a letter. That was funny. The letter had a lot of letters in it!

_____
_____
_____
_____

NOW TRY THIS!

- **What do you think this robot is saying?**
- **Write in the past then in the present tense.**

Past

Present

Teachers' note Revise the different forms of the past and present tenses of verbs (including the use of auxiliary verbs like *am, is, are, was* and *were*). Read the first example with them, ask them to identify two different types of past tense (*was shining* and *melted*) and discuss which forms of the present tense to use (*is shining* sounds right but *melts* does not – *is melting* would be better).

100% New Developing Literacy
Sentence Structure and
Punctuation: Ages 7–8
© A & C BLACK

Action sentences

Think about how each character or object might move.

- **Choose a** $\boxed{\text{doing}}$ **word and a** $\boxed{\text{place}}$ **.**
- **Write the sentences.**
- **Read the sentences.**

Doing words

trundled

tumbled

ambled

dabbled

marched

slithered

Places

across the field.

through the grass.

at the edge of the pond.

down the hillside.

along the High Street.

through the village.

The stream _____ .

A herd of cattle _____ .

The green snake _____ .

A dozen soldiers _____ .

The huge lorry _____ .

Four ducks _____ .

NOW TRY THIS!

- **Write a sentence about something else in action.**

Use interesting words.

Teachers' note Remind the children of their previous work on interesting verbs to use instead of *was* and *goes* when describing settings. Point out that interesting verbs can help to create a character in a story. Tell them that this page is about the ways in which characters move and that they are looking for interesting verbs to use instead of *went*.

**100% New Developing Literacy
Sentence Structure and
Punctuation: Ages 7–8**
© A & C BLACK

Setting sentences

- **Make sentences to describe settings**
- **Match each building to a `doing` word and a place.**

On the chart, colour the words you use. Use a different colour for each sentence.

- **Write the sentences.**
- **Read the sentences.**

Building	What the building did	Place	
Valley Farm	guarded	along the old railway.	
High House	squatted among	the town.	
Elm Street School	clung to	on a hilltop overlooking the village.	
Station Cottages	nestled in	the wall of the church.	
Priory Mews	perched on	in a hollow by a stream.	
Rook Castle	stretched along	among gas works and old warehouses.	

NOW TRY THIS!

- **Write a sentence about the setting of a building you know.**

Use interesting words.

Teachers' note Begin with three sentences about locations: for example, *The road goes through the village*, *The river goes through the gorge*, *Huge trucks go along the High Street*. Discuss other verbs to use instead of *goes*: *The road snakes through the village*, *The river rushes through the gorge*, *Huge trucks trundle along the High Street*.

100% New Developing Literacy Sentence Structure and Punctuation: Ages 7–8
© A & C BLACK

Time sentences

- **Read the sentences.**
- **Add information about time.**
- **Read the new sentences with a friend.**

Use the time-bank.

1 I found my purse _____.

2 _____ I had seen a stranger in the street.

3 _____ I thought there was something odd about him.

4 We would have to get home _____.

5 She said she would phone me _____.

6 The police had warned us about bike thieves

_____.

7 We saw Orion and other star groups _____.

8 We were glad to see our friends again _____.

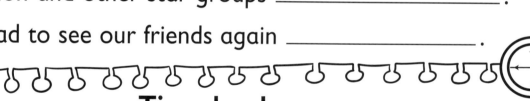

Time-bank

at first

later in the evening

only a few days earlier

that night

earlier that morning

before it got dark

after the summer holidays

later that day

NOW TRY THIS!

- **Write time sentences using these.**

| a few weeks later | in the middle of the night |

Teachers' note Read the first example with the children and discuss the purpose of the words *found* and *my purse*. *I found* says what people did and *my purse* says what they did it to. Tell them that they are going to write a word or words in the gap to say when this happened. Ask them to choose the most appropriate word/s from the time-bank.

100% New Developing Literacy
Sentence Structure and
Punctuation: Ages 7–8
© A & C BLACK

Place to place

Where might it have happened?
- **Write in the gaps.**
- **Read the sentences.**

Use the place-bank.

1 They could see a ship _____.

2 _____ a plume of smoke rose from the chimney of a farmhouse.

3 _____ two boys were picking up shells.

4 _____ her mother would be waiting.

5 It would be less windy _____.

6 He could hear the sound of a chainsaw cutting wood _____.

7 Lights glittered _____.

8 She spotted a heron wading _____.

Place-bank

in the distant village	down on the beach
across the valley	in the forest
at the edge of the pond	far out at sea
on the other side of the wall	back at home

NOW TRY THIS!

- **Write time sentences using these.**

| on the other side | in the distance |

Teachers' note Read the first example with the children and discuss the purpose of the words *They could see* and *a ship*. *They could see* says what people did and *a ship* says what they did it to. Tell them that they are going to write a word or words in the gap to say where this happened. Ask them to choose the most appropriate word/s from the place-bank.

20

100% New Developing Literacy Sentence Structure and Punctuation: Ages 7–8 © A & C BLACK

One thing after another

- **Circle the words that tell you the order in which things happened.**

Leah had to get through the Golden Door, but before that she had to pass the dragon that guarded it. Before she could get near the dragon it sensed that she was there. She hoped that the spell of protection had not worn off. After a few minutes the dragon turned away. This was her chance. She pointed the Stillit at the dragon's head. It worked instantly. The dragon was still.

Now Leah had to check what was on the other side of the door. First she pressed her ear to the door and listened. Not a sound. Then she turned the key and pushed. The door didn't budge. She pushed harder. It still didn't budge. Her next thought was that it was bolted. In a few seconds she was sliding her very fine sword through the tiny gaps around the door. She had to be quick. Before long the Merfolk would catch up with her. After what seemed like hours the sword caught on something. In a flash Leah pushed the bolt-mover through the tiny gap and moved it backwards and forwards. It took about thirty seconds to free the bolt. As soon as it had moved, she pulled the door with all her might. Straight away she knew why the door had been locked and bolted.

- **Write about what you have done today.**
- **Show the order in which you did everything.**

Teachers' note Tell the children that they are going to read a passage from a story and that their task is to look for words which tell them in what order the events in the passage happened. They can then reread the passage, with a partner if appropriate, and circle these words.

100% New Developing Literacy
Sentence Structure and
Punctuation: Ages 7–8
© A & C BLACK

Shrink it

- **Copy each sentence six times.**
- **Each time miss out a different word.**
  Is it still a sentence? ☐ ✔ or ☐ ✘

First he found a big box.

| ☐ |

_____

_____

_____

_____

_____

Ben always works very hard here.

_____

_____

_____

_____

_____

_____

I saw the old red car.

_____

_____

_____

_____

_____

_____

She plays the piano there daily.

_____

_____

_____

_____

_____

_____

NOW TRY THIS!

- **Which words can be taken out of sentences?**
- **Write on this chart.**

Can	Cannot

- **Talk to a friend about the kinds of words that can be taken out of sentences.**

Teachers' note Write up a sentence or display it on the interactive whiteboard: for example, *Six shivering snowmen sat very still*. Invite a volunteer to delete a word. Ask the others to read what remains. Does it make sense as a sentence? Repeat this, deleting a different word each time. Ask the children which words could not be deleted in order to keep a sentence.

100% New Developing Literacy Sentence Structure and Punctuation: Ages 7–8
© A & C BLACK

Shrinking sentences

- **Take words out of each sentence.**
- **Make it as short as you can.**

Check that it is still a sentence.

A young man on the train talked noisily on his mobile phone.

Three girls played skipping in the middle of the playground.

The lady wearing an extremely smart suit had lost a very expensive watch.

A small man was carrying a huge, heavy cardboard box.

A beautiful blue dragonfly hovered above the green, slimy pond.

NOW TRY THIS!

- **Add different words to this short sentence.**
  The cat stopped at the edge of the pool.
- **Make it into three _different_ sentences.**

Teachers' note Remind the children of their previous work on deleting words from sentences (page 22) and ask them to delete as many words as possible from each sentence, making sure that what remains is still a sentence. During the plenary session draw out that some types of word are essential to sentences and discuss which they are.

**100% New Developing Literacy
Sentence Structure and
Punctuation: Ages 7–8
© A & C BLACK**

Growing sentences

- **Read the short sentence.**
- **Add some words to make a long sentence.**
- **Make two different long sentences.**

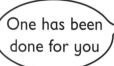 One has been done for you

1 Jack opened the book.

a _Jack opened the story book and began to read._

b _Jack opened the book and looked at the pictures._

2 Mum poured a glass of water.

a _____

_____

b _____

_____

3 The dog rushed towards me.

a _____

_____

b _____

_____

4 There was a spider in the bath.

a _____

_____

b _____

_____

NOW TRY THIS!

- **Find a sentence from your own writing.**
- **Add words to it.**
- **Make it as long as you can.**
  Does this make it a better sentence?

Teachers' note Explain that in this activity children are going to add words to sentences. Read the completed example with them and discuss the purpose of the words added: to give information about the order in which things happened. For what other purpose could words be added? Examples include to describe Jack or the book or to say how, where or when he opened it.

100% New Developing Literacy Sentence Structure and Punctuation: Ages 7–8 © A & C BLACK

You can join two sentences with $\boxed{\text{because}}$ **.**

- **Draw a line from a cloud to a flower to join the sentences.**
- **Write** $\boxed{\text{because}}$ **on the line.**
- **Write the long sentences.**

The ice cream melted.

No one heard him coming.

She had to walk home.

The computer would not work.

because

She had lost her bus fare.

He was wearing soft shoes.

It was not plugged in.

It was in a hot place.

_____

_____

_____

_____

_____

_____

_____

NOW TRY THIS!

- **Write another** $\boxed{\text{because}}$ **sentence.**
- **Split it into two shorter sentences.**

Teachers' note Remind the children of their previous work (see Year 2) on words used for joining sentences in order to make one long sentence. Ask for examples of such words: for example, *and*, *but*. Point out that sometimes part of a sentence says why something was done. Introduce the word *because* for joining two sentences where one says *why* something happens.

100% New Developing Literacy Sentence Structure and Punctuation: Ages 7–8 © A & C BLACK

25

That's why

A sentence can say why something
is done.

Put your jacket on so that you won't be cold.

Word-bank
in case
in order to
otherwise
so that
to

• **Write a why ending for these sentences.**

1 Look and listen for traffic _in case_ _____

_____ .

2 I shall lock my bike _____

_____ .

3 She put an umbrella in her bag _____

_____ .

4 They went to town _____

_____ .

5 You must buy a parking ticket _____

_____ .

6 They went into the café _____

_____ .

NOW TRY THIS!

• **Write three sentences about why you do things.**
• **Use words from the word-bank.**

Teachers' note Remind the children of their previous work on the use of *because* to join sentences
to say why something happened. Ask for examples of other words which say *why* (see the word-
bank).

**100% New Developing Literacy
Sentence Structure and
Punctuation: Ages 7–8**
© A & C BLACK

The noun test

| Common nouns | name things.

ghost   book   snail   robot

Here is the | noun test |.

Can you put | a | **,** | an | **or** | the | **in front of it?**

| ✔ | **It is a common noun.** | ✗ | **It is not a common noun.**

- **Test these words with a, an or the.**

___a___	ghost	✔
_____	sit	
_____	rubbish	
_____	blue	
_____	bike	
_____	curly	
_____	face	
_____	eat	

_____	glue	
_____	paper	
_____	sing	
_____	clever	
_____	silly	
_____	corner	
_____	brown	
_____	up	

NOW TRY THIS!

- **Underline the** | common nouns |.

A lion woke up when a mouse ran over his face. He jumped up and grabbed the mouse and was about to kill him. The mouse asked the lion to let go and said that one day it could save the lion's life. The lion laughed and let go.

Teachers' note Remind the children of their earlier work (Year 2) on words for naming things. Note that these words do not need capital letters unless they are names of people or other individual things such as countries, cities or festivals. Introduce the term *common noun* for names of ordinary things and point out that these can always have a, *an* or *the* before them.

100% New Developing Literacy Sentence Structure and Punctuation: Ages 7–8 © A & C BLACK

The right noun

- ## Find the nouns with the same meanings.
- ## Write them in the shapes.

Word-bank

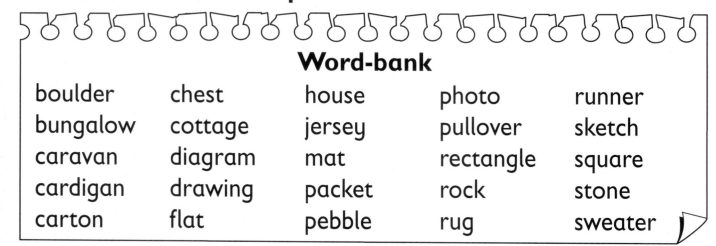

boulder	chest	house	photo	runner
bungalow	cottage	jersey	pullover	sketch
caravan	diagram	mat	rectangle	square
cardigan	drawing	packet	rock	stone
carton	flat	pebble	rug	sweater

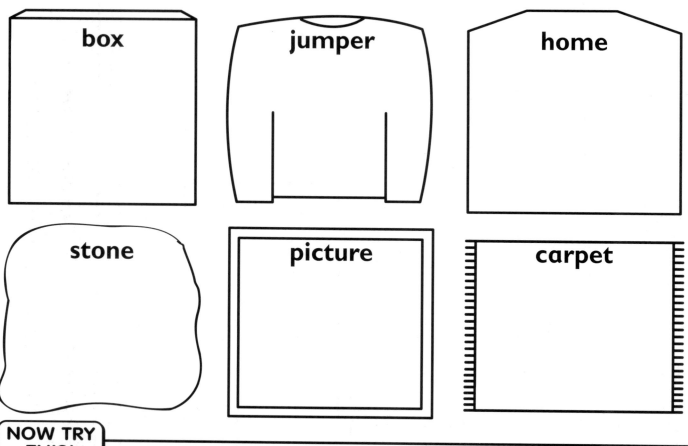

box

jumper

home

stone

picture

carpet

NOW TRY THIS!

- ## List some nouns that mean the same as these. chair   rubbish   ship

Use a thesaurus.

Teachers' note Remind the children that nouns are words which name things and explain that there are many nouns for the same type of thing but that each one has a slightly different meaning. You could ask the children to name types of shoe as an example: slipper, boot, sandal, brogue. Ask them to read the nouns in the noun-bank and to write them on the shape with a similar meaning.

100% New Developing Literacy Sentence Structure and Punctuation: Ages 7–8 © A & C BLACK

Proper noun challenge

A proper noun is a name given to a person, place, brand or date.

It begins with a capital letter.

• Fill in the chart with proper nouns .

First letter	Girl's name	Boy's name	Family name	Town or city	Sweet	Cartoon character
D			Dillon	Dundee	Drifter	Donald Duck
F						
G						
N						
R						
S						
T						

You could think of countries, rivers, singers, sports people and more!

NOW TRY THIS!

• Make up your own chart with different headings and different letters.

100% New Developing Literacy
Sentence Structure and
Punctuation: Ages 7–8
© A & C BLACK

Teachers' note Revise common nouns (pages 27–28). Note that these words do not need capital letters because they are not the names of people or other individual things such as countries, cities or festivals. Introduce the term *proper noun* for these and point out that these generally cannot have *a*, *an* or *the* before them, unless *the* is part of the name (for example, The Netherlands).

Wobbling words

You can use these words instead of names.

| he | him | | she | her | | it | | they | them |

boys   men   girls   women   things animals   more than one person, animal or thing

What is wrong with the (wobbling) words?

• Write the correct words in the boxes.

This is my Dad. (She) is thirty years old.

He had a new car. (They) was red.

Jack waved to me. I waved to (it).

Ella can run fast. (He) won a race.

My sister gave me a present. I thanked (it).

The Patels live next door. I like (they).

I washed my hair and then dried (him).

Mum made some tea and gave (him) to Sally.

NOW TRY THIS!

• Write three sentences using these words.

| he | her | it | them |

Teachers' note Revise words that are used instead of names and ask children which word they use when they talk about themselves and which one they use for someone they are talking to. Use the introductory part of this page to remind them of the words they can use for other people.

**100% New Developing Literacy
Sentence Structure and
Punctuation: Ages 7–8**
© A & C BLACK

Pronouns

You can use a │ pronoun │ instead of a │ noun │ .

Pronoun-bank

he	him	it	she	they	we
her	I	me	them	us	you

- **Copy the sentences.**
- **Write a │ pronoun │ instead of each │ noun │ .**

1 │ Ella │ kicked │ a ball │ .

_____

2 │ Harry │ said to │ Ella │ , "May │ Harry │ play?"

_____

3 │ Ella │ said to │ Harry │ , "Come with │ Ella │ ."

_____

4 │ Ella and Harry │ saw │ Parveen and Lee │ .

_____

NOW TRY THIS!

- **Write sentences using these │ pronouns │ .**

  │ I │   │ you │   │ they │

- **Rewrite the sentences using │ nouns │ .**

Teachers' note Ensure that the children have their completed copies of page 30 to hand. Ask them about the words they used instead of the names of people, animals or things. Tell them that these words are known as *pronouns*, which means *for nouns*. Draw out that if only pronouns are used, the reader cannot tell who or what a sentence is about.

100% New Developing Literacy
Sentence Structure and Punctuation: Ages 7–8
© A & C BLACK

Instead of nouns

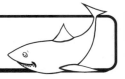

- **Instead of the** nouns **in boxes, write one of these pronouns.**

he	him	she	her	it	they	them

Minos was the King of Crete. The people of Athens had killed his son. For revenge

Minos [ ] sent for seven young men and seven young women from Athens

every four years. Minos [ ] fed the youngsters [ ] to a monster

called the Minotaur. The Minotaur [ ] was half-man and half-bull.

The Minotaur [ ] lived in a labyrinth under the palace. A labyrinth is a maze.

King Aegeus of Athens promised his people that Aegeus [ ] would put a

stop to this. King Aegeus [ ] sent his son Theseus to Crete to kill the

Minotaur. Theseus [ ] set sail for Crete. When the ship came ashore Minos

saw the ship [ ] and went to see who was in the ship [ ]. Ariadne,

his daughter, went with Minos [ ]. When Ariadne [ ] saw Theseus,

Ariadne [ ] fell in love with Theseus [ ]. Ariadne [ ] decided

to help Theseus [ ]. Ariadne [ ] gave Theseus [ ] a ball of

string. Ariadne [ ] told Theseus [ ] to take

the string [ ] into the labyrinth.

NOW TRY THIS!

- **List four other nouns from the story.**
- **Which words could you use instead?**

he	him	she	her	it	they	them

Teachers' note Read the passage aloud and ask the children to identify the nouns in it. Discuss why some of them should be replaced by pronouns (it sounds clumsy to repeat the names of people and things). Draw out why they are not asked to replace *all* the nouns with pronouns. They could try this in order to find out. They should notice that this makes the passage difficult to understand.

100% New Developing Literacy Sentence Structure and Punctuation: Ages 7–8
© A & C BLACK

Belonging

These words show belonging.

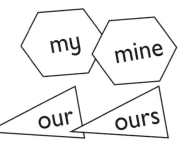

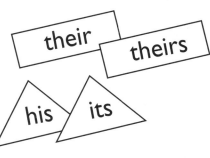
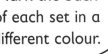

- **Cut out the cards.**
- **Turn them face down.**
- **Take turns to turn over a card from each set.**
- **Keep them if they match.**

Mark the back of each set in a different colour.

Set 1

		him
me	you	us
me	it	them

Set 2

		That is my book. The book is mine.
That is your coat. The coat is yours.	That is his car. The car is his.	That is her home. The home is hers.
That is its name.	That is our room. The room is ours.	That is their dog. The dog is theirs.

NOW TRY THIS!

- **Write sentences about things belonging to these.**

me	you	him	her	us	them

Teachers' note Remind the children of the different purposes of words in a sentence: to name people or things (or to use instead of these names), to show actions and to say where, when or why things happened. Tell them that they are going to find out about words which show belonging. Use familiar examples, such as This is *my* book, That is *your* pencil.

100% New Developing Literacy
Sentence Structure and
Punctuation: Ages 7–8
© A & C BLACK

Words for describing

These words describe someone or something.

tall

round

sad

wavy

long

soft

hot

In sentences they describe | nouns |.

- **Circle the words that describe the** | nouns |.

1 There was a tall green | plant | growing beside the small | cottage |.

2 An angry | woman | was shaking her fist at her young | son |.

3 The frightened | lad | began to climb up the enormous | plant |.

4 "The | cow | was old. This | beanstalk | is wonderful," he said.

5 He looked up and saw a pair of huge | boots |.

6 The huge | boots | were on a pair of gigantic | feet | on the ends of two massive | legs |.

NOW TRY THIS!

- **Write two sentences to continue the story.**
- **Underline the nouns.**
- **Add a word to describe each noun.**

Teachers' note Remind the children of the different purposes of words in a sentence: to name people or things (or to use instead of these names), to show actions, to say where, when or why things happened and to show belonging. Tell them that they are going to investigate words which describe things, people and places. Emphasise that these words describe nouns.

100% New Developing Literacy Sentence Structure and Punctuation: Ages 7–8 © A & C BLACK

Describe and draw

Complete the sentence. Use two words from the adjective-bank.

Here is a _____ _____ dot.

This is a _____ _____ box.

This shows a _____ _____ line.

Here we have a _____ _____ cat.

Here you can see two _____ _____ ducks.

These are three _____ _____ bells.

Adjective-bank

black

blue

fat

fluffy

happy

long

red

round

shiny

silver

tiny

yellow

NOW TRY THIS!

- **Write adjectives in the gaps.**

A _____ smell drifted through the _____ window. A _____ sound came from the _____ frying pan. Then I saw six _____ sausages.

eachers' note Remind the children of their previous learning about words that describe (page 34) nd explain that these are called adjectives. Ask them to choose the most appropriate describing ord for the nouns in the captions. Provide colouring pencils/crayons for the children to colour in he artwork to match the adjective.

100% New Developing Literacy Sentence Structure and Punctuation: Ages 7–8 © A & C BLACK

All change

- **Change the** ⬚ adjectives ⬚ **to match the pictures.**

Jack is a ⬚ smart ⬚ ⬚ young ⬚ man.

These rough square stones were on the beach.

_____ _____

_____ _____

The sea was calm and smooth.

He wore a fresh clean t-shirt.

_____ _____

I drew a long straight line.

We found a large empty box.

_____ _____

NOW TRY THIS!

- **Write four adjectives to describe these.**

    a house   a car   a street

Change the adjectives to make the descriptions different.

Teachers' note Remind the children of their previous learning about words that describe (pages 34–35) and introduce the term *adjective* if you have not done so already. The children are required to identify the two adjectives in each caption and to change them for others which better describe the picture.

**100% New Developing Literacy
Sentence Structure and
Punctuation: Ages 7–8
© A & C BLACK**

Verb detective

Help the │ verb │ detective.

- **Circle the verbs.**

Walk
run
skip

The goddess Persephone lived in Ancient Greece. Her mother was the goddess Demeter, who made all the plants grow everywhere on Earth. In those days there was no winter or autumn. It was always spring or summer.

One day, when Persephone was playing in the fields, the ground opened. A deafening sound rumbled from the hole and a chariot came roaring out. Dark horses pulled it. Hades, the god of the Underworld was riding the chariot.

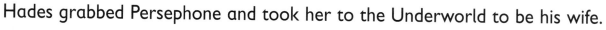

Hades grabbed Persephone and took her to the Underworld to be his wife. The hole closed behind them.

Demeter looked all over the Earth for Persephone. She became so sad that she forgot all about the plants, so they did not grow. The first winter arrived.

Then a shepherd found Persephone's belt. He took it to Demeter.

"Where did you find it?" asked Demeter. The shepherd showed her. Demeter guessed what had happened. She told Zeus, the King of the Gods, "If you don't tell Hades to let Persephone go, I will stop making the plants grow. The Earth shall have nothing but winter."

Zeus ordered Hades to free Persephone. Demeter went to meet her, but Persephone could not leave the Underworld. She had eaten some pomegranate seeds. There was an old law about this. Anyone who had eaten in the Underworld had to stay there.

Demeter thought hard. A plan formed in her mind.

NOW TRY THIS!

- **What do you think Demeter did?**
- **Write three sentences about it.**
- **Circle the verbs.**

Teachers' note Remind the children of the different purposes of words in a sentence: to name people or things (or to use instead of these names), to show actions, to say where, when or why things happened and to show belonging. Tell them that they are going to investigate words for actions and introduce the term *verb* for these words.

100% New Developing Literacy
Sentence Structure and
Punctuation: Ages 7–8
© A & C BLACK

Verb sort

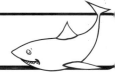

- **Cut out the cards.**
  Sort them into two sets: | nouns | **and** | verbs |.

Nouns are words for people, animals, places and things.

Verbs are words for actions.

- **Take turns to pick up a card from each set.**
- **Use them to complete this sentence.**

The girls _____ the _____.

- **Write the sentences.**

boat	cactus	car	catch
chase	climb	daisy	eggs
elephant	feed	follow	hide
hug	jelly	lamp post	mend
moon	mountain	paperclip	ride
sausages	scrub	sky	slap
snowflake	throw	tickle	weigh

Teachers' note It is useful to glue each set of words onto a different coloured card to facilitate keeping them in two sets: nouns and verbs. Remind the children of their previous learning about the purposes of words in sentences, particularly nouns and verbs, before they play the game. Note that sentences can make sense as sentences even if they say something silly.

100% New Developing Literacy
Sentence Structure and
Punctuation: Ages 7–8
© A & C BLACK

Smart verbs

- **Read the sentences.**
- **Write a different verb to match each picture.**

He cut the carrot.

He sl _____ the carrot.

He ch _____ the carrot.

He gr _____ the carrot.

She walked upstairs.

She t _____ upstairs.

She st _____ upstairs.

She st _____ upstairs.

The light shone.

The light bl _____ .

The light tw _____ .

The light gl _____ .

NOW TRY THIS!

- **Write three different verbs for these.**

| said | ran | ate | put |

Teachers' note Remind the children that verbs are words for actions and explain that there are different verbs for the same type of action but that each one has a slightly different meaning. You could ask the children for different verbs which mean *talk*: for example, whisper, chatter, gossip. Ask them about the picture each one conjures up in their minds.

100% New Developing Literacy
Sentence Structure and
Punctuation: Ages 7–8
© A & C BLACK

Vivid verbs

• **Write the verbs on the thesaurus pages. One has been done for you.**

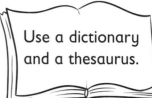
Use a dictionary and a thesaurus.

call
exclaim

mend

turn

go

~~exclaim~~

fix

set off

vanish

patch

twist

repair

yell

disappear

twirl

spin   cry

move

restore

leave

begin

shout

revolve

bellow

scream

swivel

renew   start

NOW TRY THIS!

• **Write three verbs which mean the same as these.**

| sleep | take | jump | watch |

Teachers' note Remind the children that verbs are words for actions and explain that there are different verbs for the same type of action but that each one has a slightly different meaning. You could ask the children for different verbs which mean *walk*: for example, stroll, march, stride. Ask them about the picture each one conjures up in their minds.

100% New Developing Literacy Sentence Structure and Punctuation: Ages 7–8
© A & C BLACK

Join-up jigsaw

- **These words are useful for joining parts of a sentence.**

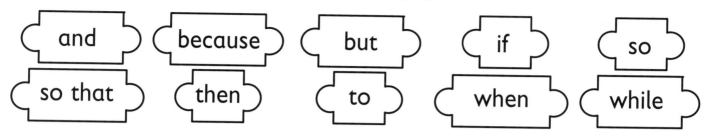

and   because   but   if   so

so that   then   to   when   while

- **Choose a word to join these to make sentences.**

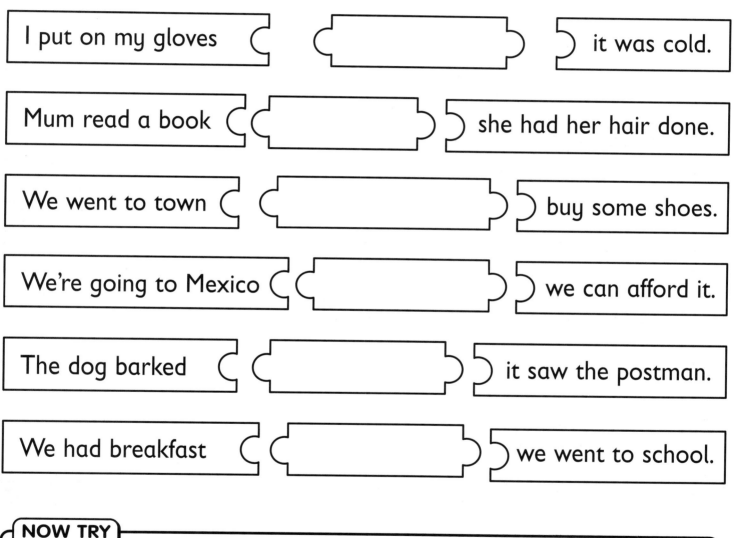

I put on my gloves   it was cold.

Mum read a book   she had her hair done.

We went to town   buy some shoes.

We're going to Mexico   we can afford it.

The dog barked   it saw the postman.

We had breakfast   we went to school.

NOW TRY THIS!

- **Write four sentences using these joining words.**

and   but   so   when

Teachers' note Remind the children of their previous work on words for joining parts of sentences (pages 24–25). Draw out that these can simply link actions or ideas or they can say when, where or why something happened. Introduce the words in the jigsaw pieces and discuss how they are used.

**100% New Developing Literacy
Sentence Structure and
Punctuation: Ages 7–8
© A & C BLACK**

Exclamation words

This is an exclamation mark $\boxed{!}$. It can show all these:

something funny

Where do snowmen dance?

At a snowball!

being pleased

Great goal!

something loud

BANG!

a surprise or fright

Eek! Aaaagh! Oh!

• **Write what they are saying. Put in exclamation marks.**

Which snakes are good at maths?

NOW TRY THIS!

• **Write a sentence about a surprise you had.**
• **Write what you said.**

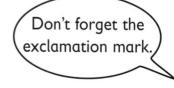
Don't forget the exclamation mark.

Teachers' note Show the children examples of sentences in books which end with exclamation marks. Discuss why there is an exclamation mark. Draw out that it is used at the end of a sentence showing shock, surprise, something funny, something frightening or that someone is pleased and surprised about something. It can follow a single word or exclamation: *Eek! Ouch! Wow! Hurray!*

**100% New Developing Literacy
Sentence Structure and
Punctuation: Ages 7–8**
© A & C BLACK

Ha, ha!

- **Match the** [questions] **to the** [answers] .
- **Put in the** [question marks] [?]
  and [exclamation marks] [!] .

What keeps a football stadium cool

Get a pencil

Two biscuits crossed the road. One got run over. What did the other one say

The fans

What should you do if your dog swallows a pen

Frostbite

What do you get if you cross a vampire with an iceberg

A jumbo jet

What do you call an elephant that flies

Crumbs

NOW TRY THIS!

- **Write another 'question and joke answer'.**

Remember the question mark and exclamation mark.

Teachers' note Revise question marks and exclamation marks. What is missing from the end of the sentence in first speech bubble? Then look at the answer to the question and ask what is missing from the end of it. Discuss why an exclamation mark should be used, rather than a full stop. Draw out that this is because it says something funny.

100% New Developing Literacy Sentence Structure and Punctuation: Ages 7–8
© A & C BLACK

End points

- **Read what the people say.**
- **Put in the full stop** `.` **question mark** `?` **or exclamation mark.** `!`

Help

First, rub the fat into the flour

May I help you

Eek   A dragon

What time is it, please

Sit

It's half past four

NEWS 24

Two men were arrested after last night's burglary

 NOW TRY THIS!

- **Put in the missing punctuation marks.**

> Come quickly My house is on fire Hello Can you hear me My name is Jack Quick Yes, that's right What did you say My address is 3 Rush Street. What

Teachers' note Remind the children of their earlier work on punctuation at the ends of sentences (Years R, 1 and 2) and discuss the types of sentences which end with full stops or question marks. Ask them to give a sentence or exclamation which would be followed with an exclamation mark and discuss its purpose (to show surprise, shock, fear, anger or that something is funny).

100% New Developing Literacy Sentence Structure and Punctuation: Ages 7–8
© A & C BLACK

Knock, knock

- **Use the joke-bank to write 'knock, knock' jokes in the speech bubbles.**

Joke-bank

Darrel

Darrel be the day.

Getta

Getta bell on this door.

Henrietta

Henrietta bag of crisps.

Knock, knock!

Who's there?

Knock, knock! Who's there?

- **Tell another 'knock, knock' joke to a friend.**
- **Write the joke, using speech bubbles.**

NOW TRY THIS!

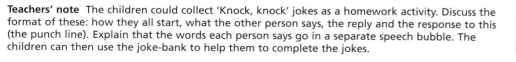

Teachers' note The children could collect 'Knock, knock' jokes as a homework activity. Discuss the format of these: how they all start, what the other person says, the reply and the response to this (the punch line). Explain that the words each person says go in a separate speech bubble. The children can then use the joke-bank to help them to complete the jokes.

**100% New Developing Literacy
Sentence Structure and
Punctuation: Ages 7–8**
© A & C BLACK

Story talk

- **Read the passage.**
  What does each character say?
- **Underline only <u>the words they say</u>.**

> Plop, the little Barn Owl – blue
> Mr Barn Owl, his father – red
> Mrs Barn Owl, his mother – green

When the very last firework had faded away, Mr Barn Owl turned to Plop.

'Well, son,' he said. 'I'm off hunting now. Would you like to come?'

Plop looked at the darkness all round them. It seemed even blacker after the bright fireworks. 'Er – not this time, thank you, Daddy. I can't see. I've got stars in my eyes.'

'I see,' said his father. 'In that case I shall have to go by myself.' He floated off into the darkness like a giant white moth.

Plop turned in distress to his mother.

'I *wanted* to go with him. I *want* to like the dark. It's just that I don't seem to be able to.'

'You will be able to, Plop. I'm quite sure about that.'

'I'm not sure,' said Plop.

'Well, I *am*,' his mother said. 'Now, come on. You'd better have your rest. You were awake half the day.'

So Plop had his midnight rest, and when he woke up, his father was back with his dinner. Plop swallowed it in one gulp. 'That was nice,' he said. 'What was it?'

'A mouse,' said Mr Barn Owl.

'I like mouse,' said Plop. 'What's next?'

'I have no idea,' his father said. 'It's Mummy's turn now. You'll have to wait till she gets back.'

From *The Owl Who Was Afraid of the Dark* Jill Tomlinson

NOW TRY THIS!

- **What do you think the owls said next?**
- **Write what each owl said.**

> Think about how to show the words they said.

Teachers' note Revise speech bubbles. Point out that only the spoken words are in the speech bubbles. Ask them to read the passage and to find the words people say. Ask how the words are marked out from the rest of the sentence. Point out the use of *said* to introduce or end speech and note that the spoken words are surrounded by speech marks.

100% New Developing Literacy Sentence Structure and Punctuation: Ages 7–8
© A & C BLACK

If animals could talk

• **Read what the characters said.**

1
Uh, oh – humans wearing silly hats. Watch out.

Yes – they might have dogs, too.

2

Something should be done about dogs that chase us.

We could get the cattle to help.

3
We can take a short cut. Sheep won't harm us.

No – but the cattle might.

4

Eeek! A bull!

That will keep them out.

• **Between the speech marks, write what they said.**

The sheep were munching grass, minding their own business, when along came a group of people.

"_____," said a sheep.

"_____," said another sheep, "they_____."

"Something _____," said the first sheep.

"We _____," answered the second sheep.

Someone opened the gate and said, "We can _____

_____."

"_____," muttered the first sheep.

The bull came charging into the field to help.

"_____," yelled the people.

"_____," said the bull.

NOW TRY THIS!

• **Look for a short comic strip.**
• **Write the dialogue, using speech marks.**

Teachers' note Remind the children of the use of speech marks to surround speech and words such as *said* to introduce or follow the spoken words. Ask them what the first sheep says. Draw out that only these words should be written between the speech marks.

100% New Developing Literacy Sentence Structure and Punctuation: Ages 7–8 © A & C BLACK

Television talk

Will Burntull talked to Mikkel on the television news.

Will: Good morning, Mikkel. You're the first wheelbarrow race champion I've met. Tell us about this wheelbarrow.

Mikkel: It began as a normal wheelbarrow – the kind you'd use in the garden.

Will: Well, it's not like <u>my</u> wheelbarrow.

Mikkel: No. We changed the shape to make it streamlined. We made it lighter, too.

Will: The wheel looks different too.

Mikkel: Yes. It's very light, but bigger than on a normal wheelbarrow.

- **Between the speech marks, write what they said.**

" _____

_____ ,"

said Will Burntull.

" _____

_____ ," said Mikkel.

" _____ ," said Will.

" _____

_____ ," said Mikkel.

" _____ ," said Will.

" _____ ," said Mikkel. "It's_____ "

NOW TRY THIS!

- **Write your own short interview with a friend.**

Teachers' note Ask volunteers to read the parts of Will and Mikkel. Discuss how they know what to say. Point out that play scripts do not have speech bubbles or speech marks; the spoken words follow the speaker's name. You could point out how this is made to stand out from the spoken words (usually in bold or upper case).

100% New Developing Literacy Sentence Structure and Punctuation: Ages 7–8 © A & C BLACK

Scriptwriter

- ## Read the passage with a friend.
- ## Write it as a playscript.

The Wind said to the Sun, "I am much more powerful than you. Watch how hard I can blow."

"No. I am more powerful than you. Watch how brightly I can shine."

"I don't know what's happening to the weather," said a man down below. "The forecast said it would be calm and cloudy."

The Wind said to the Sun, "I can get that man's coat off him but you can't."

"Yes, I can," said the Sun.

"We'll see," said the Wind, and he blew and blew.

Character	What he or she said
Wind	_____
Sun	_____
Man	_____
Wind	_____
Sun	_____
Wind	_____

NOW TRY THIS!

- ## Write the next two lines of the script.
- ## Rewrite them using speech marks.

Teachers' note Give the children copies of their completed page 48 in addition to a copy of this page and ask them to compare the play script and the dialogue they wrote using speech marks. Ask them what they did to convert this dialogue into a play script.

100% New Developing Literacy
Sentence Structure and
Punctuation: Ages 7–8
© A & C BLACK

Speech marks

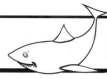

Speech marks are used instead of a speech bubble.

Would you like to be my friend?

Nina

Nina said, "Would you like to be my friend?"

"Yes!" said Toby.

Yes.

Toby

• **Write the words between the speech marks.**

What is your favourite book, Raj?

Simon

I like <u>The Sheep Pig</u> by Dick King-Smith.

Raj

That's the book of the film <u>Babe</u>.

Emily

"What's _____," asked Simon.

"_____,"

said Raj.

"_____," said Emily.

NOW TRY THIS!

• **What could Simon ask Raj about the book?**
• **What might Raj answer?**
• **Write what they say.**

Use speech marks.

_____

_____

Teachers' note Remind children of the purpose of speech marks and ask them to look at the other punctuation marks in the sentences. Draw out that they always come just before a speech mark and explain how commas, question marks or exclamation marks are used to end the spoken part when the sentence continues with *said* or another word for *said*.

**100% New Developing Literacy
Sentence Structure and
Punctuation: Ages 7–8**
© A & C BLACK

Speech on the page

- **Look carefully at the speech bubbles and the sentences with speech marks.**
- **What differences can you see? Talk to a friend about them.**
- **Circle them in red.**

Mum said she'll take us swimming.

Gemma

Great. I'll go and ask Dad if I can come.

Tara

"Mum said she'll take us swimming," said Gemma.

"Great," said Tara.

"I'll go and ask Dad if I can come."

- **Write what they say.**
- **Use speech marks.**

Bring your bike. There's a safe place to ride them near our house.

Tom

Ok. I'll be there at about 2 o'clock.

Dan

NOW TRY THIS!

- **Write a phone conversation using these.**

Teachers' note Remind children of the purpose of speech marks and ask them to look at the other punctuation marks in the sentences. Draw out that they always come just before a speech mark and explain how commas, question marks or exclamation marks are used to end the spoken part when the sentence continues with *said* or another word for *said*.

100% New Developing Literacy Sentence Structure and Punctuation: Ages 7–8
© A & C BLACK

The comma store

• **Show the comma keepers where to put commas.**

She bought a loaf two oranges a melon and a bag of sugar.

I counted four sparrows six wagtails twelve swallows and ten bluetits.

At the new leisure centre we can swim play tennis or football and learn judo.

We know how to use full stops question marks exclamation marks and commas.

At the fair there were roundabouts dodgem cars hoopla donkeys and a roller coaster.

Ants bees wasps flies ladybirds and beetles are all insects.

NOW TRY THIS!

• **Write a sentence listing what you did before you set off for school today.**

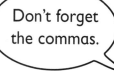 Don't forget the commas.

Teachers' note Remind the children of their previous work on commas in lists and demonstrate how they are useful by reading the first unpunctuated list. Note that the last item in the list has *and* before it and point out that there should be no comma there because *and* is used instead of the last comma.

100% New Developing Literacy
Sentence Structure and
Punctuation: Ages 7–8
© A & C BLACK

The first person

I am the first person.

So am I.

So are we.

The [first person] means [I], [me], [we] or [us].

- **Which sentences are in the** [first person] **?**
- **Tick them.** ✔

Ella is two years old. ☐

I am two years old. ☐

I have two brothers. ☐

They are called Deepak and Alankar. ☐

We have six classes in our school. ☐

It is a big school. ☐

You must have a lot of children in your school. ☐

I'll send you a picture of my school. ☐

You can look at our school website. ☐

I'll have a look now. ☐

NOW TRY THIS!

- **Write three sentences about you, your family and your school.**
- **Write in the** [first person].

Teachers' note Remind the children of their previous work on nouns and pronouns and ask them about the words they use for themselves (*I, me*) and for themselves in groups (*we, us*). Use the introductory section of this page to introduce the first person (you could enact this in a humorous way with three other adults).

100% New Developing Literacy
Sentence Structure and
Punctuation: Ages 7–8
© A & C BLACK

The second person

 **You are the second person.**

So are you!

So are you!

So are you!

The [second person] **means** [you].

- **Write these sentences in the** [second person].

One has been done for you.

1 I live in London

You live in London.

2 I have six brothers.

_____

3 I could help Mum.

_____

4 We washed our hands.

_____

5 We should close the gate.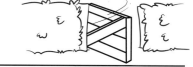

_____

6 I could ask my dad to take me.

_____

NOW TRY THIS!

- **Write three sentences addressed to a friend.**
- **Write in the** [second person].

Write three nice things about your friend.

Teachers' note Remind the children of their previous work on nouns and pronouns and ask them about the words they use for someone they are talking to (*you*). Use the introductory section of this page to introduce the second person (you could enact this in a humorous way with three other adults).

100% New Developing Literacy Sentence Structure and Punctuation: Ages 7–8 © A & C BLACK

The third person

He is the third person.

She is the third person.

So are they.

It is the third person too.

The third person means these:

| he | him | she | her | it | they | them |

- **Write this recount in the** | third person |.
- **Change the underlined words.**

<u>I</u> called for Harry and Reena and <u>we</u> walked to the shops to spend <u>our</u> pocket money. On the way <u>we</u> saw a car parked outside Hamish's house. <u>We</u> wondered whose it was. Then <u>we</u> saw Hamish at the window. He waved to <u>us</u> and <u>we</u> waved back. <u>I</u> asked Harry and Reena to come with <u>me</u> to see Hamish.

"Hamish might want to come with <u>us</u> to the shops," <u>I</u> said. So <u>we</u> strolled up the path and knocked. <u>We</u> could hear a bumping sound in the hall. <u>We</u> strained <u>our</u> ears to hear better. <u>We</u> waited for a while and then a man <u>we</u> had never seen before opened the door.

_____

_____

_____

_____

_____

NOW TRY THIS!

- **Write three sentences about someone from history.**
- **Write in the third person.**

Teachers' note Remind the children of their previous work on nouns and pronouns and ask them about the words they use for someone or something they are talking about (*he, him, she, her, it*) and for a group of people or things (*they, them*). Use the introductory section of this page to introduce the third person (you could enact this in a humorous way with four other adults).

100% New Developing Literacy Sentence Structure and Punctuation: Ages 7–8 © A & C BLACK

Reporting sentences

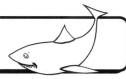

These sentences are from a report.

- **Underline the** │ verbs │.
- **Circle the** │ pronouns │:

(I) (me) (we) (us) (you) (he) (him) (she) (her) (it) (they) (them)

Plants are living things.

They make their own food.

They need air, water, and sunshine.

Some plants grow in shady places but they need some light.

Animals are living things.

They have to find food to eat.

A sunflower

- **Tick the correct answers.**

  The sentences are in the past ☐ tense.

  present ☐

  They are in the first ☐ person.

  second ☐

  third ☐

NOW TRY THIS!

- **Write three sentences about plants you know.**
- **Use the** │ present │ **tense and the** │ third │ **person.**

Teachers' note Revise previous work on verbs and person. Ask children what they know about verbs and remind them of the past and present tenses. Also remind them about the pronouns and verb forms used in the first and third person. Draw out that non-chronological reports are usually written in the present tense and in the third person.

100% New Developing Literacy
Sentence Structure and
Punctuation: Ages 7–8
© A & C BLACK

Do this

Which sentences give instructions? ✔

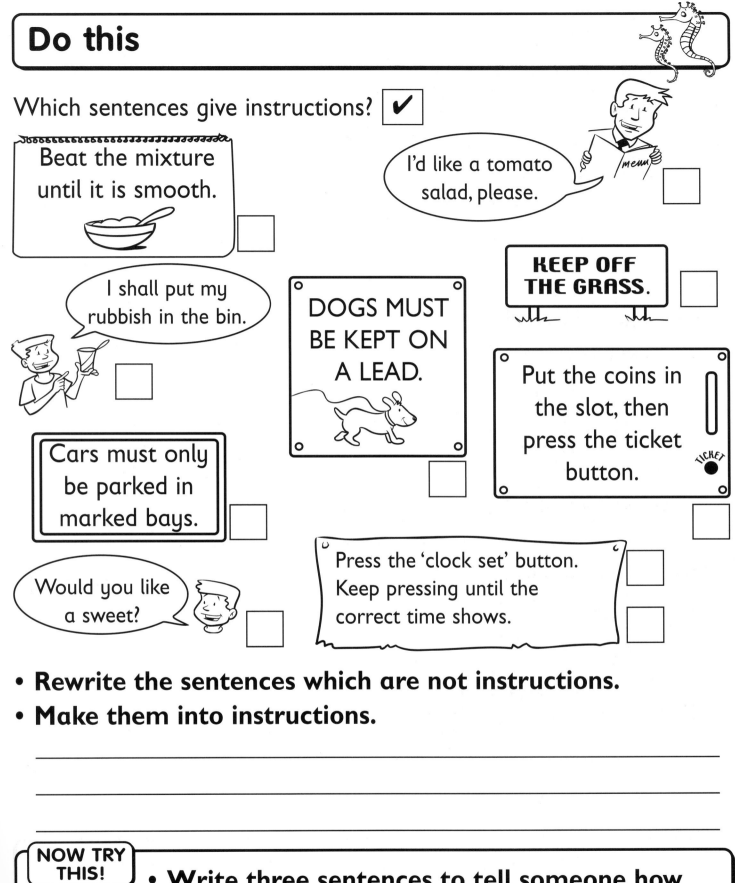

Beat the mixture until it is smooth. ☐

I'd like a tomato salad, please. ☐

I shall put my rubbish in the bin. ☐

DOGS MUST BE KEPT ON A LEAD. ☐

KEEP OFF THE GRASS. ☐

Put the coins in the slot, then press the ticket button. ☐

Cars must only be parked in marked bays. ☐

Would you like a sweet? ☐

Press the 'clock set' button. Keep pressing until the correct time shows. ☐

- **Rewrite the sentences which are not instructions.**
- **Make them into instructions.**

_____

_____

_____

NOW TRY THIS!

- **Write three sentences to tell someone how to sharpen a pencil.**

Teachers' note Revise different types of sentence and their purposes: giving a recount, asking a question, giving information, giving instructions. Read the first example with the children and ask what kind of sentence it is. Draw out that it is an instruction because it tells the listener or reader what to do. Point out how the verb differs from the verb in a story or information sentence or a question.

100% New Developing Literacy Sentence Structure and Punctuation: Ages 7–8 © A & C BLACK

Command verbs

- **In the boxes write** | verbs | **that give** | instructions | .

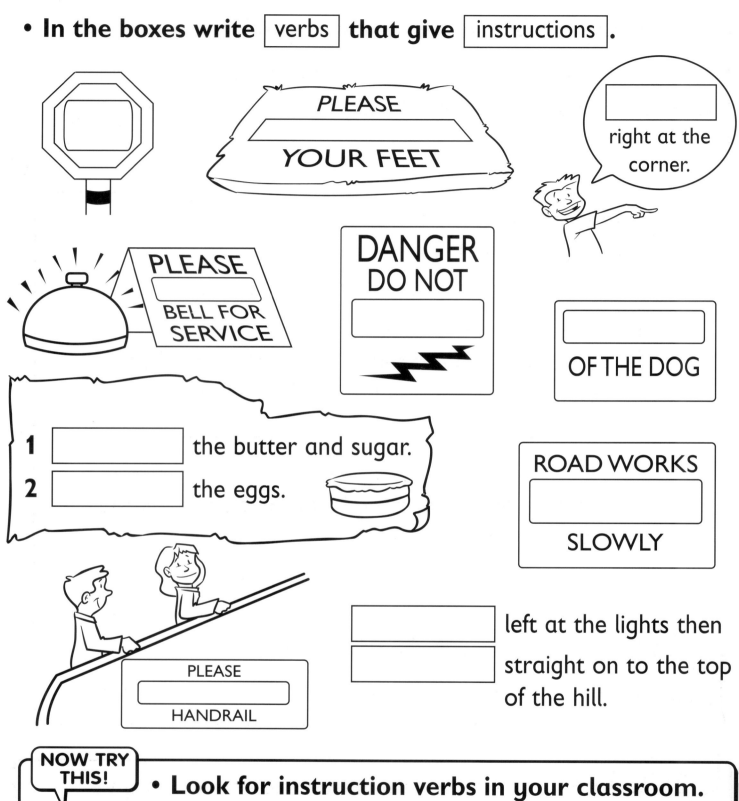

PLEASE

YOUR FEET

right at the
corner.

PLEASE

BELL FOR
SERVICE

DANGER
DO NOT

OF THE DOG

1   the butter and sugar.

2   the eggs.

ROAD WORKS

SLOWLY

PLEASE

HANDRAIL

left at the lights then

straight on to the top
of the hill.

NOW TRY THIS!

- **Look for instruction verbs in your classroom.**
- **List six instructions.**
- **Draw boxes around the** | verbs | .

Teachers' note Remind the children of their previous work on instructions and verbs. Ask what they know about the verb in an instruction sentence. Complete the first example with them by asking them if they know what the object is (a road sign). Ask what they might see written on a sign which has this shape (*Stop*). Point out that *Stop* is an instruction or command.

**100% New Developing Literacy
Sentence Structure and
Punctuation: Ages 7–8
© A & C BLACK**

That's the way

Elli is talking about her journey to school.

- **Change each sentence to an instruction.**
- **Circle the words you will change.**
- **Rewrite the sentence.**

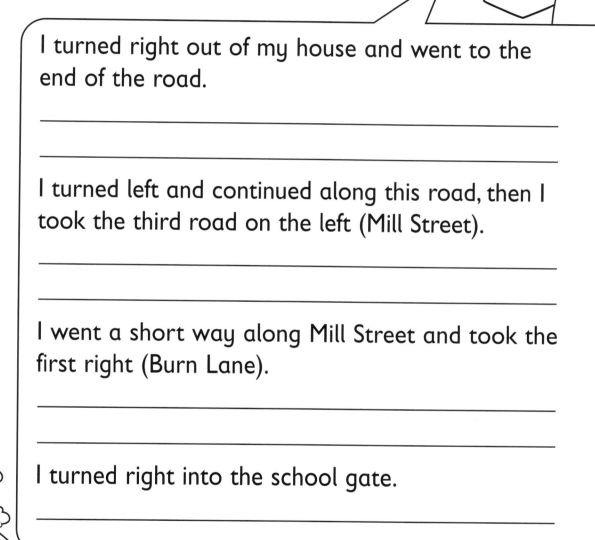

I turned right out of my house and went to the end of the road.

_____

_____

I turned left and continued along this road, then I took the third road on the left (Mill Street).

_____

_____

I went a short way along Mill Street and took the first right (Burn Lane).

_____

_____

I turned right into the school gate.

_____

NOW TRY THIS!

- **Write three instruction sentences to give directions to somewhere you know.**

Teachers' note Read the first example with the children and ask then what kind of sentence this is: question, instruction, information or recount. How can they tell? Focus on the verb: note that it is in the past tense and that it says what the writer did. It is a recount (story sentence). Discuss how it could be changed into an instruction to tell someone how to find their way.

100% New Developing Literacy Sentence Structure and Punctuation: Ages 7–8 © A & C BLACK

Go with the flow

- **Read the sentences.**
- **Join them with** | time words |.
- **Write the long sentences you have made.**

> You might have to change the capital letters and full stops.

| As soon as | → | Santa Claus woke up. He knew it was Christmas Eve. |

_____

_____

Time-bank

as soon as

first

then

while

| | → | He fed his reindeer. |

| He ate a healthy breakfast. | ← | |

_____

_____

| | | The elves began to wrap the toys. Santa got out his red suit. |

_____

_____

NOW TRY THIS!

- **Write three sentences about Santa Claus.**
- **Use these** | time words |.

| meanwhile | | next | | when |

Teachers' note Remind the children of the purposes of different words in sentences: to say what someone or something does/did (verb), to name something (noun), to replace a noun (pronoun) or to say where, when or how something happened. Ask which would be the most useful type of word when putting the events of a story in order (words to say when something happened).

100% New Developing Literacy Sentence Structure and Punctuation: Ages 7–8 © A & C BLACK

Sentences in poems

Some poems are not written in sentences .
Capital letters might not be only at the
beginnings of sentences.
Full stops might be missing.

Use different colours.

- **Underline the sentences .**

From *The Owl and the Pussy Cat*
By Edward Lear

The Owl and the Pussy Cat went to sea
In a beautiful pea-green boat,
They took some honey, and plenty of money,
Wrapped up in a five-pound note.

From *Child's Song in Spring*
By Edith Nesbit

The silver birch is a dainty lady,
She wears a satin gown.
The elm tree makes the old churchyard shady,
She will not live in town.

The English oak is a sturdy fellow,
He gets his green coat late.
The willow is smart in a suit of yellow,
While the brown birch trees wait.

- **Write them on the lines.**

NOW TRY THIS!

- **Talk to a friend about why poems are not always in sentences.**

Put the capital letters and full stops in the correct places.

Teachers' note Point out that poems need not be written in sentences but that many poems contain sentences. Read the first example with the children so that they can enjoy the rhythm and humour. Ask them which parts of it are not sentences, and how they can tell. Can they find any sentences? They can then underline and copy the sentences.

**100% New Developing Literacy
Sentence Structure and
Punctuation: Ages 7–8
© A & C BLACK**

Non-sentences

- **Cross out some words so that these are not** sentences .
- **Make them sound like lines from poems.**
- **Write the lines.**

Work with a friend.

The first one has been done for you.

Sentence	Poetry line
We could hear the hurry of hooves in the village street.	The hurry of hooves in the village street
I can hear a swish, swash, swish, swash as the wipers wipe the windscreen.	
I am floating as if I am weightless in the deep, dark pool.	
What a big flame came from that little scratch of a tiny match.	
The wolf crept by, looking very lean and very mean.	
I can see lightning flashing in the sky and hear thunder crashing in the distance.	
There is a heron standing by the pond, as still as a picture, watching the fish.	

NOW TRY THIS!

- **Write three sentences to describe a scene.**
- **Make them into lines for a poem.**

Teachers' note Read the first example with the children and ask if it sounds like a line of poetry. Draw out that the first part could be omitted, leaving *The hurry of hooves in the village street.* (The words *We could hear* are not needed and the line sounds better without them.)

100% New Developing Literacy Sentence Structure and Punctuation: Ages 7–8 © A & C BLACK

Poem without a sentence

- **Read the sentences.**
- **Make them into a poem.**
- **Cross some words out.**
- **Read what is left.**
- **Write it to look like a poem.**

Work with a friend.
Discuss your ideas.

My hands grip the handlebars. One foot is on a pedal. I am wondering if I dare to speed down the hill. I think it will be fun. I can feel the wind rushing through my hair. I imagine going faster and faster. I can feel my heart beating. I can hear the wheels whirring. However, I know about the danger. I have no safety helmet on. Will I be able to stop at the bottom? Shall I lift the other foot? Shall I give a push?

NOW TRY THIS!

- **Turn a short passage from a story into a poem.**
- **Take words out. Change the layout.**

Teachers' note Discuss what the text is about and point out that the description can be made more effective by writing it in lines of poetry, some of which need not be sentences or parts of sentences and some of which could be questions or exclamations. During the plenary session invite volunteers to read their poems aloud. Discuss which words have been changed and the effects of these changes.

**100% New Developing Literacy
Sentence Structure and
Punctuation: Ages 7–8**
© A & C BLACK

A sentence in any shape

- ## Write sentences about these:

  | a snake | | a tower | | a tree |

- ## Practise on scrap paper.
- ## Choose a shape to write each sentence on.

NOW TRY THIS!

- ## Draw three other shapes to write sentences on.
- ## Give them to a friend to write one.

Teachers' note Encourage children to use scrap paper for writing words to describe the appearance of the subject and how it affects people, animals or its surroundings. These could include expressive verbs to create an impression of how the subject moves or how it exists: for example, *nestles, towers, looms, slithers, glides.*

100% New Developing Literacy Sentence Structure and Punctuation: Ages 7–8 © A & C BLACK